A WOODLAND MYSTERY™

The Hunt for Pirate Gold

A WOODLAND MYSTERY

By Irene Schultz

The Wright Group®

To my aunts Dorothy and Cora, with whom I'd love to go adventuring

The Hunt for Pirate Gold
©1996 Wright Group Publishing, Inc.
©1996 Story by Irene Schultz
Cover and cameo illustrations by Taylor Bruce
Interior illustrations by Meredith Yasui, Tom Boatman, and Charles Solway
Map illustration by Alicia Kramer

Woodland Mysteries™
© Wright Group Publishing, Inc.

The Woodland Mysteries were created by the Wright Group development team.

The Wright Group
19201 120th Avenue NE
Bothell, WA 98011

Printed in the United States of America

10 9 8 7 6 5

ISBN: 0-7802-7236-6

What family solves mysteries...has adventures all over the world...and loves oatmeal cookies?

It's the Woodlanders!

Sammy Westburg (10 years old)
His sister Kathy Westburg (13)
His brother Bill Westburg (14)
His best friend Dave Briggs (16)
His best grown-up friend Mrs. Tandy
And Mop, their little dog!

The children all lost their parents, but with Mrs. Tandy have made their own family.

Why are they called the Woodlanders? Because they live in a big house in the Bluff Lake woods. On Woodland Street!

Together they find fun, mystery, and adventure. What are they up to now?

Read on!

Meet the Woodlanders!

Sammy Westburg

Sammy is a ten-year-old wonder! He's big for his fifth-grade class, and big-mouthed, too. He has wild hair and makes awful spider faces. Even so, you can't help liking him.

Bill Westburg

Bill, fourteen, is friendly and strong, and only one inch taller than his brother Sammy. He loves Sammy, but pokes him to make him be quiet! He's in junior high.

Kathy Westburg

Kathy, thirteen, is small, shy, and smart. She wants to be a doctor some day! She loves to be with Dave, and her brothers kid her about it. She's in junior high, too.

Dave Briggs

Dave, sixteen, is tall and blond. He can't walk, so he uses a wheelchair and drives a special car. He likes coaching high-school sports, solving mysteries, and reading. And Kathy!

Mrs. Tandy

Sometimes the kids call her Mrs. T. She's Becky Tandy, their tall, thin, caring friend. She's always ready for a new adventure, and for making cookies!

Mop

Mop is the family's little tan dog. Sometimes they have to leave him behind with friends. But he'd much rather be running after Sammy.

Table of Contents

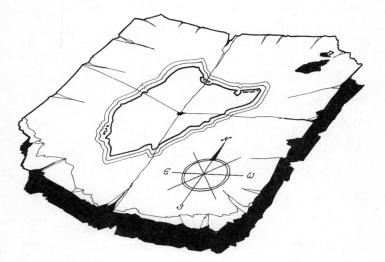

Chapter 1:
The Treasure Map

Ten-year-old Sammy Westburg's eyes shot
open.

He was on the floor of a condo in
Florida.

He rolled over off his air mattress.

He yelled, "Ouch! Some thing's been poking me! ALL OVER! ALL NIGHT!"

He jumped up and ran over to the big pull-out bed.

Two boys were sleeping on it. One was Sammy's fourteen-year-old brother Bill. The other was their sixteen-year-old friend Dave Briggs.

Sammy jumped up on their bed and kept on jumping.

He yelled, "The air went out of my air mattress! I had to sleep on a bunch of bumps! You were in the comfortable bed! It was terrible!"

2

Bill looked at his watch and laughed.

He said, "It was terrible, huh? Then how come you slept so late? It's ten o'clock already."

Dave said, "Ten? You're kidding! We better get up and eat. Chief Hemster's plane gets in right after twelve."

He pulled himself out of bed and into his wheelchair.

Bill fixed the sheets and blankets. Then he folded up the pull-out bed. They all got ready to go.

His sister Kathy came out of the next room.

So did Mrs. Tandy.

The five of them called themselves the Woodlanders.

Mrs. Tandy said, "What's all the noise out here?"

Sammy waved his fists. He shouted, "That air mattress is a bumpy mess.

3

And Bill doesn't even give a hoot! He even laughed!"

Sammy's face was red.

Mrs. Tandy gave him a hug.

She said, "Well, maybe he will give a hoot about breakfast. Let's go, so we make it to the airport on time!"

Sammy said, "Sure, Mrs. T., I know you can't wait to see Chief Hemster. He's your number-one boyfriend!"

Mrs. Tandy said, "No, honey, YOU'RE my number-one boyfriend!"

They left the condo and went out to their rental car. Bill and Sammy folded Dave's chair and put it in the back. They all piled in.

Soon they were sitting around a table at a nearby restaurant.

Kathy took out a copy of an old-looking map of Mexico.

Bill said, "Good thinking, Kathy. You brought the treasure map! I still can't believe you found that, Dave."

Dave said, "But you're the one who bought the diary. Three hundred years old. Amazing."

Kathy said, "But Dave, you're the only one who believed the diary could be true."

Dave said, "Well, when I read what that sailor wrote about Cozumel ... and the treasure maps ... and pirate gold ... I WANTED to believe it!"

5

Dave said the name like this: KOH-zuh-mel.

He went on. "I went through the diary about twenty times, looking for a map. I couldn't find one. It was you who noticed the front cover was coming apart, Kathy."

Kathy said, "But remember? I wanted to glue it back together!"

Sammy said, "That map would have been stuck inside the cover forever! See? Being neat can cause a lot of trouble."

Mrs. Tandy said, "Well, YOU'LL never have that trouble, Sammy. In fact, right now there's grape jelly on your nose."

Sammy said, "Boy, I can't wait to fly to Cozumel and find that gold. Good-bye Florida ... hello, Mexico!"

He waved his fork around in excitement. Half a fried egg flew off of it ... landed on his bare leg ... and slid to the floor.

Bill dipped his napkin in his water glass and cleaned off Sammy's leg.

Sammy yelled, "Hey! That's cold! Cut it out!"

Kathy said, "Sammy, quiet down! Everyone's looking at us."

Sammy said, "Well, then make Bill stop drowning me."

Dave said, "Here, Sammy, help me figure out this map. Everything's in Spanish. Why do you think the treasure is marked with an X and the words ORO CON LOS DIOSES?"

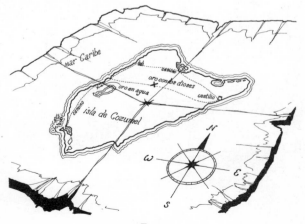

Mrs. Tandy said, "I think that means 'gold with the gods.'"

Dave said, "And this other X is marked ORO EN AGUA."

Sammy said, "AH-gwuh?"

Dave nodded. "In Spanish, AGUA means water. And ORO means gold. And EN means in."

Kathy said, "So that part means 'gold in water.'"

Sammy said, "I still think it means the gold is in that lagoon ... that little lake on the map. Or maybe it's in the ocean."

Dave said, "But the X isn't in the lagoon ... or the ocean. The X is BETWEEN them."

Bill said, "Yeah, Sammy, the gold HAS to be on land."

Sammy said, "Maybe the sailor meant the pirate gold was first in the water ... and then moved to land.

"Or maybe he buried it in a bottle of water!"

Bill laughed. He said, "Maybe so. Well, come on, Sammy. It's time to meet Chief Hemster's plane."

He put his arm around his brother. He said, "You get to ride in the front seat. And I'll fix you up a soft bed tonight from the couch pillows.

"And it's my turn to sleep on the no-air mattress. Chief Hemster gets the couch bed with Dave. So cheer up!"

And off they drove to the Florida airport.

■   ■   ■

But there was something they didn't know. A man with a red beard was following them in his car.

Chapter 2:
Fish Brains?

The Woodlanders stood waiting in the airport.

Before they knew it, Police Chief John Hemster came through the gate.

Sammy ran up to him and hugged him hard.

Chief Hemster said, "Whoa, there, Sammy! I think you broke three ribs with that hug!"

Sammy said, "Well, I had to get my hug in first. I was afraid when you saw Mrs. Tandy, you'd never stop hugging HER."

He began singing, "Mrs. T. has a BOY-friend."

Mrs. Tandy just smiled and said, "Well, how about you and Jill Wilson back in Bluff Lake?"

Sammy didn't say another word.

Dave said, "We have a surprise for you, Chief! Our plane to Mexico isn't until tomorrow at ten. So right now we get to go fishing!"

Chief Hemster said, "That sounds like fun! Let's go!"

Mrs. Tandy drove them to the fishing dock.

Dave bought each of them a ticket for the boat.

Then Chief Hemster and Bill lifted Dave and his chair onto the boat.

The others sat down on long benches.

One of the passengers was a red-bearded man. He sat down next to them.

When the boat left the dock, the red-bearded man said, "Hello, there! I'm Tom Snow. How's it going?"

Dave said, "Hi! Where are you from, Mr. Snow?"

The man said, "New York. I'm flying to Mexico tomorrow for a vacation. Cozumel, in fact."

"COZUMEL!" the Woodlanders all said at the same time.

Dave said, "That's where we are going, too!"

Mr. Snow said, "What luck for me! I don't know anyone on the island. Maybe we will run into each other."

Then he said, "Look at those big birds on those posts. Pelicans. See? There's one diving for a fish!"

The big bird came back up out of the water. It had a huge, bag-like bill.

Mr. Snow said, "I love pelicans. They're the only things around that can eat more fish than I can."

Sammy laughed. He really liked this stranger.

Soon it was time to start fishing.

The fishing rods were heavy. Mr. Snow showed Kathy an easy way to handle the reel.

He helped Sammy get a tangle out of his line.

He gave them all some of his sunflower seeds to eat.

Sammy said, "These are good. Hey, how long are we going to be out here? I'm getting hungry."

Bill said, "Don't worry. They sell cookies and soda pop on the boat."

Then Mr. Snow felt a tug on his line. He lifted his fishing pole high up in the air to hook the fish.

But when he reeled in his line, nothing was on it.

His bait was all chewed up.

He put on the new bait fish, and gave his old one to Sammy.

He said, "Wave it in the air. That's it.

Now the pelican sees it. He's coming close. Throw it into the air in front of him."

Sammy did.

The pelican flew down in a rush.

It caught the chewed-up fish right at the top of the water.

Bill said, "Wow! Look at that!"

A minute later, Kathy yelled, "Wait! Something's on my line!"

She started reeling it in as hard as she could.

Everyone jumped out of Kathy's way.

The captain ran over with a long pole. The pole had a big hook on one end.

Kathy pulled her fish closer to the boat. Now she could see it in the water.

It was big and silvery and beautiful.

The captain hooked it through its side.

Dark red blood ran out of the hole in its silver skin.

The captain said, "It's a kingfish. And a beauty, too."

Sammy said, "That's horrible! I didn't know it would be so bloody and horrible to kill it. I'm never going to fish again."

Mrs. Tandy said, "It IS sort of horrible. That's why I'd only kill an animal if it were going to hurt me, or for food."

By then, every person on the boat had come to look at Kathy's fish.

17

Then they ran back to their fishing rods. They wanted to catch one just like it.

And so did Sammy, after all.

He ran over and picked up his pole.

Chapter 3:
Fish Poison

Sammy let out his line.

He said, "That kingfish was really after MY line. Kathy got hers in the way.

"Now I'M going to catch one!

"Hey! Hey! Something's on my line!" Then he shouted, "Rotten rats! It's just a little one!"

He pulled up his pole, and the fish flopped onto the deck.

It was about as long as his shoe. Its red fins looked like fancy wings. It flopped around, gasping for air.

Sammy shouted, "It's beautiful! It's much better than an old kingfish!"

He raced over to pick it up.

Mr. Snow yelled, "Don't, Sammy! Don't touch it!"

He ran over and grabbed Sammy's line. He let the fish hang over the side of the boat.

Then he took a big fishing knife from his belt. He cut Sammy's line.

The fish flopped back into the water.

Sammy was mad.

He yelled, "That was MY fish! It was better than Kathy's! A lot better. And you threw it away!"

Mr. Snow said, "I'm sorry, Sammy. I had to. It was a scorpion fish. If you'd picked it up, it would have poisoned you.

"Its fins are sharp ... with poison as strong as a scorpion's."

Sammy said, "Poison! I was going to grab him! And you saved me! I'm sorry I got so mad."

21

Mr. Snow said, "That's OK. Let's see what else you can catch ... and not another scorpion this time!"

A minute later, everybody was yelling.

The boat had passed through a whole school of kingfish.

Mrs. Tandy, Chief Hemster, Dave, Bill, then Kathy, landed one.

At last a fish took Sammy's bait. It was so big, Mr. Snow had to help him land it.

Before they knew it, it was time to head back to the pier.

Sammy said, "I don't ever want this day to be over! I'm going to throw in my line one last time."

But his bait fish never went under the water. A great big pelican flew down and grabbed it.

The hook stuck in the bird's beak.

The pelican fell into the water.

The line was twisted around the end of its wing. Its wing and beak were pulled together.

Sammy screamed, "It's going to drown!"

The captain yelled, "Cut the line, quick!"

Dave yelled, "No! Then the hook and line will stay stuck to the pelican!"

Sammy jumped onto the pier.

The captain yelled, "Hey! Come back here with that rod!"

Sammy ran down the pier to the sandy beach, dragging the pelican after him. Mr. Snow, Bill, and Kathy were right behind him.

Mr. Snow ran into the water and grabbed the pelican.

Bill ran over and pulled open the bird's beak.

Kathy reached right into its big mouth. She worked the hook and line loose.

She said, "Don't let go, you guys. There's another hook in its mouth, a rusty one. And here's another one!"

When the pelican was all fixed up, they let it fly away.

Mr. Snow said, "That was great thinking, kids. And Kathy, you did that like a doctor."

Kathy smiled up at him.

Sammy said, "That's what she wants to be when she grows up!"

They all walked toward the parking lot.

Mrs. Tandy said, "Mr. Snow, thank you for all your help."

Sammy said, "Yeah, thanks a lot! Hope we see you in Cozumel. But we will be busy looking for—"

Suddenly EVERYONE poked Sammy to stop him from talking.

Bill pulled him into the car.

Sammy was so mad, he was kicking.

He said, "Leave me alone! I wasn't going to tell him about the treasure map and the pirate gold.

"And anyway, he likes kids. He's OK. Didn't you see how he helped us? What's wrong with you guys?"

Dave said, "I'm sorry, Sammy, but Mr. Snow isn't who he pretends to be. He's a fake!"

Chapter 4:
A Surprise Lagoon

Dave said, "In fact I KNOW he was lying to us. I even know who he is."

They all said, "You KNOW him?"

Dave said, "Yes! He's not from New York. He's from Bluff Lake. Our town!

He used to coach Little League when I was Sammy's age.

"He's not Tom Snow. He's Tom Sanders."

Chief Hemster said, "Why, Dave, you're right! I've seen him around town for years. But I didn't realize it was Sanders. That red beard sure had me fooled."

Mrs. Tandy said, "Well, NOW what do we do? Is he here just by chance? Or is he following us?"

Sammy said, "How could such a nice guy be such a dirty lying rat?"

They left the condo early the next day.

At 10:00 in the morning they were back at the Florida airport.

There was Mr. Sanders, the FAKE Mr. Snow. He was even taking the same plane they were!

He smiled and said, "Good morning,

everybody!"

Sammy had set a heavy metal fishing box on the ground.

Mr. Sanders picked it up. He said, "I'll carry this for you, Sammy."

Sammy ran up and grabbed the box. He said, "Keep your hands OFF!"

Mr. Sanders said, "OK, OK! Boy, Sammy's in a bad mood today!"

No one answered him.

They all boarded the plane.

Sammy, Chief Hemster, and Bill played cards the whole plane trip to Cozumel.

Kathy was sitting in the row in front of them ... next to Dave and Mrs. Tandy.

She looked down at the bright water.

She said, "That water sure looks great."

Sammy said, "I know, I can hardly wait. The first thing I want to do after we land is swim in the ocean."

Bill said, "OK, if you don't care about finding the pirate gold. But I think we should rent a car first ... and drive around the island."

Sammy said, "OK, big boss. I'll do that first. But THEN I'm going swimming in the ocean."

Their plane landed.

The hotel bus picked them up.

At the hotel, they un-packed, then went down to the front desk to rent a car.

They bought a new map of Cozumel. The island looked tiny next to Mexico!

Dave said, "Who's driving ... Mrs. Tandy or Chief Hemster?"

Mrs. Tandy said, "I'd love to drive. Four-wheel-drive cars are so much fun!"

So they put Dave's wheelchair in the back, and piled in.

Sammy shouted, "Let's GO! Let's explore in a hurry! I WANT TO SWIM IN THE OCEAN!"

They drove around to the south-west. They found the lagoon that was on their old map.

Bill said, "Our guide book says it's a surprise lagoon."

31

Sammy said, "What kind of surprise could a little lagoon have? NOW can we go swimming in the ocean, please?"

Chief Hemster said, "Let's keep on driving for a while."

But right away they came to the edge of a jungle. The road ended.

Bright blue parrots darted from tree to tree.

Kathy said, "I'd love to walk into the jungle. But I guess we should look at the other roads."

Sammy said, "When do I get to swim in the OCEAN?"

They turned and drove past the lagoon again, toward their hotel. They came to a side road that seemed to go right into the jungle.

Dave said, "Hey, doesn't this road look like it's headed for ORO CON LOS DIOSES on our treasure map?"

Sammy said, "Well, sort of. I'll take a look down the road with you ... but THEN I want to go swimming in the ocean."

Mrs. Tandy steered up the rocky jungle road. Branches brushed the sides of the car.

The car began to bump around so much, they had trouble talking.

Bill said, "I feel like a ... hailstone ... when it hits ... the ground."

Kathy said, "I feel like a ... rubber ball."

Sammy said, "I ... feel like ... a jumping bean."

33

Mrs. Tandy said, "This whole road ... is made of ... big lumps of coral."

Chief Hemster said, "I ... bet we are the ... only ones crazy enough ... to drive up this road."

Sammy said, "I can ... see why! My hip bones ... just pushed up ... to my neck. At least no one ... will bug us here while ... we look ... around."

But Mrs. Tandy said, "I wouldn't ... count on ... that.

"I just looked ... in the rear-view mirror.

"A car is ... following us ... through the jungle!"

Chapter 5:
Snow in the Jungle

Sammy turned his head around as far as
he could.

He looked at the car coming after
them.

"Hey!" he shouted. "It's Mr. Snow! Oops. I mean Mr. Sanders!"

Mrs. Tandy said, "What should we do?"

Dave said, "Let's stop. Let's find out what he's up to, once and for all."

Chief Hemster said, "Good idea, but be ready for trouble."

So Mrs. Tandy pulled to a stop.

Tom Sanders drove his car right up in back of theirs.

He got out.

He said, "Am I glad you stopped! A few more miles of this road and I would have been a milkshake."

Bill said, "You're glad? Why were you following us? We know you're not Tom Snow, Mr. Sanders. So what do you want?"

Mr. Sanders said, "Well, I hope my beard fools the men I'm after better than it fooled you."

Chief Hemster said, "The men you're after? What do you mean?"

Mr. Sanders said, "I'm here on secret business. I need your help, Chief Hemster. And perhaps your friends' help, too.

"I work in an office in Bluff Lake. But that's just my cover. I really work for the U.S. Army."

He pulled out some papers from his wallet.

37

Chief Hemster looked at them and nodded.

Mr. Sanders went on. "Someone's been stealing secrets from the army base.

"We think it's a spy who's getting paid in diamonds ... smuggled in through Mexico.

"We don't know how the diamonds come into the U.S. But we have reason to believe they come through Cozumel."

Sammy shouted, "Cozumel! That's here!"

Mr. Sanders went on. "I found out that you were coming here, Chief Hemster.

"And I learned that the Woodlanders would be with you.

"I wanted to ask for your help before. But I didn't get a chance to speak to you alone on the boat ... so here I am now.

"What do you say?"

Chief Hemster said, "Well, we are here on a kind of secret business of our own. But if you run into trouble, you can count on me.

"And I'm sure you can count on the Woodlanders, too.

"Just let us know when you need us."

Mr. Sanders thanked them.

He said, "Now I'll let you go on your way ... wherever you were going!"

He followed them until he found a wider place in the road.

Then he turned around and drove away.

The Woodlanders went bumping along again.

Sammy said, "Boy, am ... I glad about Mr. Sanders. I would ... hate for someone so ... nice to be a ... crook. But I knew ... he was OK all along."

Bill said, "Oh ... sure you did, Sammy.

Well, anyway, I'm glad, too. I hope we ... can help him."

At last the road got a little wider, then turned a corner.

Mrs. Tandy slammed on the brakes.

The road ENDED!

Sammy took one look and yelled, "What a rip-off!"

In front of them was a little stone hut.

It was filled with dirt.

It was almost covered with dead vines.

Sammy said, "A stupid hut! We drove an hour and a half. We scrambled our brains. We bounced like tennis balls.

"And what for? For some old beat-up stone house, that's what!

"NOW can we give it up? NOW can we go swim in the ocean?"

Dave said, "Wait a minute, guys. Look at the size of those stones. They're huge! No one would work THAT hard just to build a house. There are plenty of trees to use for houses."

Kathy nodded. "Dave's right. This must have been some kind of special place. Maybe early Mexicans built it for their gods."

Mrs. Tandy said, "Then the gold could be here! The ORO CON LOS DIOSES!"

Bill said, "But this hut is so small. I thought the early Mexicans built big temples ... huge ones.

41

"A large room of stone, then a smaller one on top of it. Then maybe another smaller one, like steps. Pretty soon they'd have a pyramid."

Dave said, "That's IT! Maybe this is the top of a pyramid! It's been covered by dirt and plants. But the rest is there, down below!"

Kathy said "Then the gold IS probably buried here somewhere. But where?"

Sammy said, "Oh, rats! There goes our treasure. We could NEVER find it and dig it out on this trip!"

Kathy said, "You're right. But wait, Sammy. You're forgetting the other gold we have to find ... the X between the lagoon and the ocean! Let's go!"

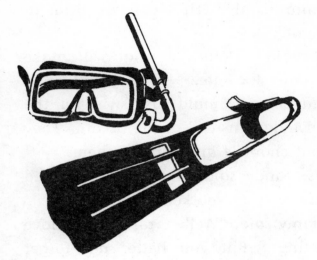

Chapter 6:
Flippers and Snorkels

Dave said, "At least we still have another chance to find gold.

"Let's get back to the hotel for our swim suits.

"Then we can look for the land where the X would be, near the lagoon."

Sammy said, "THEN can we swim in the ocean?"

Bill said, "Doing all that will make dinner way too late.

"Maybe we should just swim in the lagoon today, instead of the ocean. They rent out snorkels and flippers there."

Mrs. Tandy said, "I've always wanted to learn how to snorkel!"

Sammy said, "Well ... all right. I love snorkeling. But you better not forget about the ocean!"

Bill said, "With you as a broken record, how could we?"

So they headed back to the hotel.

Bump. Bump. Bump.

It took more than an hour to get out of the jungle.

Back in their hotel rooms, they put on

their swimsuits.

By then it was 4:00 in the afternoon.

They drove back to the lagoon.

They tried to walk to the spot between the lagoon and the ocean. But a thick jungle kept them out.

Finally Sammy said, "Let's forget the gold for now. I'm as hot and sticky as a chewed-up gumdrop."

Bill said, "Me, too. Let's head for the lagoon!"

They rented flippers and snorkels.

Mrs. Tandy said, "So how do you work this snorkel, anyway?"

Dave explained, "You just put this part of the tube in your mouth. Hold it with your teeth and breathe through it.

"The other end of the tube stays in place ... above the water."

Sammy said, "It's easy. You swim along a few inches under the water.

45

Keep your eyes open.

"You can see everything down below you. And you don't have to keep coming up for air!

"But if you DO go down, don't breathe in!"

The Woodlanders carried Dave in his chair right into the water.

Then he tipped forward out of it, and swam off.

They brought the chair back to shore. They left it with the man who ran the snorkel stand.

In a few minutes they were all swimming around.

But Chief Hemster went down deep!

He sucked in a mouthful of water.

He began coughing and spitting.

Sammy and Bill stayed with him until he was OK. Then they tried snorkeling together.

Sammy saw a school of silvery fish go by.

He got so excited, he started to talk.

The snorkel came out of his mouth.

He had to stand up to blow water out of the snorkel tube.

Just then he heard a horrible scream. It came from the other side of the lagoon.

It was Kathy!

Sammy grabbed Bill's arm. He pulled it hard.

Bill came up to the top of the water.

Chief Hemster followed him.

Sammy said, "Come on! Something's wrong with Kathy!"

They found Dave and Mrs. Tandy.

They all raced across the lagoon.

Kathy looked as pale as a fish's belly.

She said, "I saw some thing in the water that scared me. I thought I was going to fall."

Sammy said, "That's IT? But you can't fall in water. Water holds you up!"

Dave said, "Are you OK now, Kathy?"

He took hold of her hand.

Her color came back.

In fact, she turned as pink as a sun set.

Mrs. Tandy said, "Show us what scared you, honey."

Kathy said, "You're not going to believe it. I hardly can. Follow me."

She lowered her head and began to snorkel along.

The others followed her.

The next minute Sammy darted up to the top of the water.

He let out a scream that was twice as loud as Kathy's.

"EEEE-YOW-W-W-W-W!"

Chapter 7:
The Underwater Caves

No wonder Kathy and Sammy screamed.

Snorkeling along, Sammy had seen the smooth sand under him disappear.

Suddenly there were black, rocky holes

below him. They were caves! Underwater caves!

He felt like he was going to fall into
them.

When Sammy screamed, a small,
skinny boy swam over from the edge of
the lagoon.

He looked about ten years old, maybe
younger. He said, "OK, what is wrong?
Why you scream?"

By then the others had come to the top of the water.

The boy said, "My name Marco. OK, what is you name?"

Sammy said, "I'm Sammy. Hey, have you seen what's DOWN there?"

Marco laughed. "Sure, I know. I here every day. It scare you? OK, you come. I show better caves to you and your friends."

He looked so friendly, Sammy liked him right away.

And Marco didn't seem scared by the caves, so Sammy felt better.

He poked Bill and said, "Let's go with him!"

Bill said, "Good idea. Come on, everyone!"

They swam after Marco. He led them to even bigger caves.

They could hardly believe their eyes.

Inside and above the caves swam wonderful fish.

Some were almost as big as Sammy! Some were as small as a finger. Some were solid colors. Some had stripes ... or spots. Kathy and Dave came up out of the water at exactly the same time. They laughed.

Kathy said, "These fish come in every single color there is!"

Dave said, "I know! And every shape! I saw some that were perfectly flat. And some with fins shaped like flowers!"

Marco led the others up for air.

He laughed when he saw everyone's faces. He said, "Big surprise, right? This surprise lagoon!"

Dave said, "Marco, where do all these fish come from? I know they can't all live in this little lagoon."

Marco said, "OK, I tell you at dinner.

I have dinner with you? Then I tell you why fish here, OK?"

Then, with hardly a splash, he slid under the water.

They followed him.

Soon he pointed to a long, scary-looking, snake-like fish.

Sammy swam away from it, fast.

The fish swam away from him, faster!

After that Sammy stayed right next to Bill. In fact, he held on to Bill's ankle!

Suddenly a HUGE gray fish zoomed out of a cave. It swam straight over toward Bill and Sammy.

It looked right into Sammy's eyes. It opened its huge mouth.

Sammy took one look inside and shot up in the water ... so fast he pulled Bill with him, ankle first.

Marco and the others saw what happened. They came up laughing.

Sammy felt silly.

Bill tried to make him feel better, so he said, "That thing scared the heck out of me! It had a mouth as big as a hippo's!

"It's lucky Sammy pulled me away from him.

"Let's get out. I've had enough of the lagoon for today. Let's take Marco to dinner! Come on, Sammy."

Sammy hit Bill on the arm and said, "I TOLD you we should go swimming in the ocean."

Back at the hotel dining room, they saw Mr. Sanders.

Dave said, "Why don't we ask him to eat with us?"

Sammy went over and got him.

They started talking, and Marco started eating.

First Marco ate a hamburger, then all

56

his french fries. Then he ate the lettuce and tomato from his hamburger plate.

Mrs. Tandy gave him half of her fries. He gobbled them down.

So Mr. Sanders ordered Marco another hamburger, and he ate all of that!

Marco said, "OK, that very good hamburgers. Now I feel OK. You are nice man, Mr. Sanders."

He moved his chair closer to Mr. Sanders and sat down again.

Dave said, "Now, Marco, what about these fish? They look like ocean fish to me."

Marco grinned. "You smart, Dave. OK, those ocean fish."

Mrs. Tandy said, "Well, goodness! How do they get into the lagoon then?"

Kathy said, "From the lagoon to the ocean it's all thick jungle!"

Marco said, "OK, I tell you. For the fish, easy. They have a way under the jungle to swim from ocean to lagoon, OK? Water run under the ground, under jungle.

"Fish know it. They swim through for something special, for taste of fresh water!

"Fresh water spring comes into lagoon. That why they go there.

"Long time ago two men follow fish

... into cave hole in ocean. One man make it to lagoon. He say there two places with air to breathe in tunnel under the water.

"The other man no make it. He never swim out.

"OK, his friend is sad. So he never tell which cave hole in ocean go to lagoon. He scared some other person try swim, and die. No one know where it is."

Dave said, "Wait a minute! Hey, guys, I have to talk to you for a second. You, too, Chief Hemster.

"Marco, Mr. Sanders, we will be right back."

He left the table. The others followed him.

Dave whispered, "You know that X on our treasure map? And the words ORO EN AGUA ... gold in water?"

Sammy said, "Sure, what about it?"

Dave said, "I bet the gold is in THAT water ... the water in the underground passageway from the ocean to the lagoon.

"That X must be over a part of the underwater tunnel!"

Chief Hemster said, "And that tunnel sounds way too dangerous to go into."

Mrs. Tandy said, "Good grief! Between this, and that pyramid, we may never find ANY gold!"

Dave said, "I know. It's not looking good. But maybe Marco can help us."

He went back to Marco. He said, "To-morrow we want to look in the ocean for that cave hole. Will you help us?"

Marco said, "After we eat breakfast, we go? Then I help?"

Sammy said, "Sure! HOORAY! At last I'll get to swim in the ocean!"

Chapter 8:
The Ocean Search

It was 7:00 in the morning.

Something grabbed Bill's big toe.

Bill kept his eyes closed.

He knew it was Sammy.

He said, "Aw, come on, Sammy. What do you think you're doing?"

Sammy said, "I'm just showing you what the ocean will be like today. This is a crab grabbing your toe."

Bill took a look at his watch. He said, "Come on, Sam the Crab. It's time to meet Marco!"

They jumped into their swimsuits.

They woke up Dave and Chief Hemster. Kathy and Mrs. Tandy were already awake next door.

When everyone was ready, they all hurried down to the front of the hotel.

They looked around.

Suddenly Sammy pointed to the side-walk. There was a small blanket-covered body on the ground ... against the hotel wall.

From under the blanket a little arm waved at them.

Sammy called, "Marco?"

Bill said, "Marco! What are you doing on the ground? Didn't you go home last night?"

Marco said, "I am home. This my home. All Cozumel my home. We eat in hotel now? Yesterday you say it OK."

He put his head through a hole in the blanket. The blanket hung down front and back, like a coat.

For breakfast, Marco ate seven pancakes.

He ate four strips of bacon.

Then he finished off with two eggs ... and two glasses of milk.

He said, "Now I am very OK."

Sammy said, "You eat more than I do and you're as skinny as a stick! And I'm as round as a balloon!"

Marco said, "We both OK like we are. Now, come on. We find cave hole, OK?"

They all crowded into the four-wheel drive.

First Mrs. Tandy drove to the scuba stand.

Dave said, "We won't need snorkel tubes. We will be diving too deep to use them."

So they just rented masks and flippers.

They drove past the jungle to the beach.

Bill and Chief Hemster carried Dave in his chair into shallow water.

Kathy bent down to pick something up off the sand. She said, "Shells! Look at these great shells!"

Then she called, "And look what I almost stepped on!"

She reached down and came up with a little starfish.

Sammy said, "Let me hold it! HEY! It sort of grabbed me! Help!"

The starfish stuck to Sammy with tiny rubbery suckers.

Kathy peeled it off gently and put it into the water.

Dave said, "Let's get in and start looking!"

He lowered himself into the water.

Bill and Chief Hemster carried the wheelchair back to the car.

Marco had them swim after him along the shoreline.

He stopped below a cliff.

Bill said, "We'd never even know where to start without Marco. You can't even see the lagoon from here."

In front of the cliff, the water was about four feet deep.

Marco and Sammy had to stand on tip-toe to keep their heads above water.

Mrs. Tandy stuck out two feet above the water!

Marco said, "OK. Tunnel start along here, under the water."

They took a deep breath and dived down to have a look.

Soon they zoomed back up.

Sammy said, "Hey! It's ALL caves down there! How do you know which one of them leads to the lagoon?"

Marco said, "I don't know. Nobody know. You find right one, OK?"

So they dived down and stared into each cave ... to see if one had a tunnel at the back. But the caves were too dark inside to see much.

After an hour Sammy said, "Hey, how do you know this is even the right cliff, Marco? There are other cliffs pretty near us."

Marco said, "I know from what old people say.

"They remember the day the man die.

"They don't know what cave ... but they tell me this is the cliff, OK?"

67

They stood and rested for a while. The morning sun threw a bright light across the water. It was hard to see anything.

Sammy said, "Duck your head under and then open your eyes. It's easier to SEE under the water. That's why they call it the SEA! Get it?"

The rest of the Woodlanders groaned at his joke.

Sammy said, "I love the ocean. I always think the saltwater will hurt my eyes. But it feels even better than lake water."

Kathy said, "That's because ocean water is like your tears. Salty."

Sammy said, "Tears? What tears? Not MY tears!"

Just then Mrs. Tandy gave a little scream and called, "My lands! LOOK AT THAT!"

She pointed toward the sun ... to a flat rock sticking out of the water.

The sun hurt their eyes, but they tried to look.

They could make out a shiny black thing.

It was as big as a person.

It was climbing up onto the rocks.

Sammy shouted, "Let's get out of here!" He began to swim toward the beach.

But Marco grabbed Sammy's feet.

And he wouldn't let Sammy get away!

Chapter 9:
Turtle Man

Marco yelled, "It OK! It OK!"

By then everyone had figured out
what the lumpy thing was.

It was a man in a black wetsuit.

The lump was a scuba tank on his back.

Marco waved to him. He called out, "Hi, Turtle Man!"

The man on the rock waved back. "Hi, OK-Marco. How's my buddy? Who do you have there with you?"

The next minute he was standing in the shallow water next to Marco.

He smiled and said hello.

Marco said, "These my American friends. This Chief Hemster and this the Woodlanders. They looking for something."

Then he said, "This Turtle Man. His other name Bob Duffy. He help sea turtles. He count them, too. He call me OK-Marco."

The man said, "Call me Duffy. Everybody does."

Sammy said, "Why do you count turtles?"

Duffy said, "To see how many there are left. They need help. Years back there were hundreds of thousands of them.

"But people killed and ate them for years. And ate their eggs. And made jewelry from their shells.

"Just a few years ago, they were almost all gone. So countries got together and made new laws to save them.

"Now, thank goodness, the count seems to be going up."

Kathy said, "How do you keep track of them?"

Duffy said, "Well, we get reports from fishing boats. And we count the turtles on the beaches at egg-laying time.

"And when I find a turtle laying eggs, I put a radio sender on her. A satellite picks up the signal." He said the word like this: SAT-el-lite.

"That way we can learn where she travels. I do more than work with the turtles, though ... I raise money to go on with my work.

"Now how about you folks? What are you looking for?"

Marco said, "My friends, they looking for way to lagoon under the water. Many fish get there from ocean. How? I don't know.

"One man swim through, long ago."

Mrs. Tandy said, "We've tried to look into the caves. But they're dark."

Kathy nodded. "We can't tell which one might have an opening to the passageway."

Duffy said, "Well, what do you know? You just answered a question that's been bugging me."

Dave said, "What do you mean?"

Duffy said, "Lots of times I see fish swimming into these caves. But they swim into ONE cave more than the rest.

"I wondered about that one. One day I swam into it with a light. There was a big tunnel opening at the back.

"I swam in and came to a second cave. It was big, with several openings in ITS back wall. It even had a large air space above the water.

"But I turned around and came back out. I was alone. I was afraid I'd get into trouble."

Bill said, "You're kidding! Where was

it? That could be the cave we are looking for!"

Duffy said, "I can point it out. Follow me!"

They followed him down.

After a little way he stopped. He shined his light into a cave.

In its back wall was a hole bigger than a doorway.

They all swam back up for air.

Duffy said, "That's the start of the tunnel. Say, do any of you scuba dive? Because then I could show you the second cave. It's at the end of this tunnel."

Dave said, "I do ... or did. I can't move my legs anymore ... but my arms are strong. I'm still a pretty good swimmer."

Duffy said, "Car accident?"

Dave nodded.

Duffy said, "Well, if you think you can

do it, why don't we give it a try? I've got all the scuba gear you'll need."

Dave stayed in the water, while Duffy led the others to his small boat.

Then Duffy helped Dave into scuba gear.

Dave said, "It feels great to do this again."

The others swam back to the cliff.

Duffy said, "Here we go, Dave!"

He handed a light to Dave. He turned on his own light and dived down.

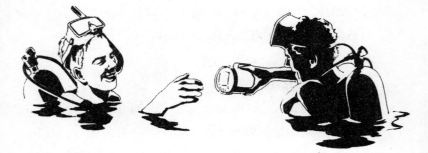

Dave followed him ... into the cave ... then into the wide tunnel.

Their lights hit the golden-white walls around them.

They swam twelve feet or so. They reached the second cave, and came up in the air space above the water.

Duffy said, "Come take a look at the back wall."

They swam under the water again.

Along the wall was a group of large holes.

A fish swam out of one of them.

Duffy and Dave came back up.

Dave said, "THAT must have been the right tunnel!"

Then a fish swam out of another.

Duffy said, "But maybe THAT one is it."

Dave said, "Maybe all these holes lead to the lagoon. But which one could a person fit through?"

Duffy said, "It's too risky to try each tunnel. What if one got smaller? We could get stuck in there and die.

"I think we should head back. But before we do, tell me, why are you so eager to find this place?"

Dave said, "I can't say right now. I hope we can tell you later. But thanks for taking me. For one thing, you showed me I can still scuba dive!"

Back with the others, Duffy said, "I have to get going. Nice to meet you all ... Chief Hemster ... Woodlanders. Maybe I'll see you again!"

Marco helped him load the scuba gear into his boat.

That gave Dave and the others a chance to talk.

Sammy said, "What did you find? What did you see?"

Dave said, "Well, we saw a bunch of

holes down there ... but it's impossible to tell which hole is the right one.

"It seems like the sailor who wrote the diary should have mapped the passageway, too."

Bill said, "Hey! Maybe he DID map it, and the map got lost. Remember in his diary? He talked about more than one map."

All of a sudden Kathy touched Bill's arm.

She said, "Listen, Bill!

"You and Dave just gave me an idea!

"Maybe there IS a way to find the gold!

"But first I have to look at something.

"Let's get back to the hotel! Fast!"

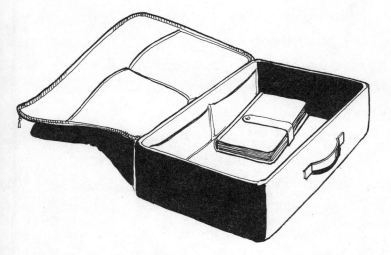

Chapter 10:
The Second Map

They rushed Dave to the car.

Marco asked, "Why you hurry? You
see another big fish in water? Or ghost?"

Kathy said, "No, but Bill and Dave

gave me an idea about a ghost ... a three-hundred-year-old ghost."

Marco looked puzzled, but he said, "OK!" and got into the car.

At the hotel Dave said, "Marco, we have to go up to our room for a while. It's nearly lunchtime. Could you eat again now?"

Marco said, "I can eat any time."

Dave said, "Then here's some money for lunch. We will be down in a few minutes, OK?"

Marco said, "OK, good, I see you then. Thank you!" Then he smiled wide and said, "Hey! There Mr. Sanders!"

Mr. Sanders waved.

Marco ran over and hugged him.

He said, "Look, I have money, OK? Now I buy YOU hamburger."

He led Mr. Sanders to the dining room.

The Woodlanders and Chief Hemster followed Kathy up to their hotel rooms.

Mrs. Tandy said, "I'm as wet as a dish rag. But I'm not changing my clothes until we hear Kathy's idea."

Kathy said, "Dave, let me see the old diary, will you?"

Dave pulled the sailor's diary out of his suitcase.

Kathy said, "Get me your knife, OK, Bill?"

Sammy called, "I'll get it!"

He ran to Bill's drawer. He grabbed a pocketknife. He handed it to Kathy.

Bill said, "Hey, Sammy, how did you know where it was? Do you have to get into EVERYTHING of mine?"

Sammy didn't have a good answer. So he stuck out his tongue.

Meanwhile, Kathy was cutting open the back cover of the diary.

She pulled the two layers apart and looked inside.

With a big smile on her face, she pulled out a piece of yellowed paper.

She said, "I KNEW it! I should have thought of this earlier ... the day Dave found the map in the FRONT cover!"

She opened the paper.

It was another map!

Everybody cheered.

Sammy did a wild dance around the room.

Kathy looked at the map closely. She said, "It's the lagoon end of the island, drawn large. See?"

She pointed to the word OCEANO near one edge ... and the word LAGUNA near the other.

She pointed to a crooked line between them.

She said, "This zig-zag MUST be the passageway!"

Dave said, "Look at this circle at one end of it. See, near the ocean. Maybe it stands for the second cave, the one that Duffy showed me."

Bill said, "And look at those little circles inside it. One of them's marked with an X."

Mrs. Tandy said, "Could they be the openings you saw, Dave? The different tunnel openings?"

Dave said, "That's it! The circles

probably DO match the openings. And the X shows which one to go into. I bet I can find it if Duffy will help me!"

Sammy said, "You hope! But what if that sailor drew the map wrong?"

Chief Hemster said, "You will need Duffy's help, Dave.

"You can't risk swimming into the wrong tunnel by mistake. Without leg control you might not be able to back out."

Sammy pointed to the middle of the crooked line. There was a large circle drawn on it, with an X inside.

He said, "What's THAT for?"

Bill said, "That's where ORO EN AGUA was written on the other map. I bet it's the gold in the water!"

Kathy said, "Well, what do we do next?"

Sammy said, "That's easy. We have lunch! I'm HUNGRY. Come on!"

Dave said, "First let's find Duffy. He has the gear and he's an expert diver. He's just the person we need."

They hurried to the hotel lobby. Duffy was just walking in the door.

Bill said, "Listen, guys. I think we should tell him our secret. I think we can trust him not to blab about the pirate gold. Or steal it."

Chief Hemster said, "I think so, too."

Sammy said, "Sure we can trust him. Marco does. And he's known the Turtle Man for a long time."

Kathy said, "Any person who tries to save turtles is OK with me."

Dave said, "Me, too."

Mrs. Tandy said, "I think he will want to help us."

They invited Duffy to lunch. They told him about the diary. They told him about the treasure maps, and asked him to help them find the gold.

And he said yes!

So they decided to start the hunt that afternoon.

Just then Mr. Sanders and Marco came over to the table.

Mr. Sanders said, "Marco bought me a hamburger ... the best I ever ate."

Marco said, "Then HE buy me back TWO hamburgers.

"And he say he buy me THREE for dinner!

"OK if I go fishing with him for afternoon? Maybe you need me, you feel bad?"

Sammy said, "No problem, Marco. We can see you tonight."

Marco smiled, and trotted into the lobby.

Mr. Sanders said, "He's a great little kid. My wife and I love children, but we never had any. It's a real treat to have him around."

Duffy said, "It's a treat for him, too, believe me.

"His mother died about four years ago, when he was six. He's had to take care of himself ever since.

"He has no other family. But he never complains. He always says—"

"—he's OK!" the Woodlanders all said at the same time.

Duffy laughed. "You got it!"

Mr. Sanders said, "Well, Marco's waiting for me. I'd better go soon.

"But first I have something very

important to tell you, Chief Hemster.
And the Woodlanders, too.

"Can we meet somewhere?

"Right away?"

Chapter 11:
Gold in Water

Duffy said, "You folks want to talk alone?
No problem. I'll just go check my gear."
   He walked away.
   Chief Hemster said, "What's up, Tom?"

Mr. Sanders said, "I found out about a boat that comes to Cozumel from time to time. It sails from Brazil.

"And it's made the trip each time army secrets are stolen."

Sammy said, "Oh, wow! Do you think it brings the diamonds to pay the spy?"

Mr. Sanders said, "Well, more army papers were missing a week ago. And the boat came in yesterday again.

"We think it carries the diamonds, all right.

"But we don't know what happens to them. The crew never comes to land.

"They anchor at night near the lagoon end of the island ... like they did last night.

"Then they leave early in the morning ... like they did this morning."

Chief Hemster said, "So they MUST have

gotten rid of the diamonds. But how?"

Mr. Sanders said, "If you come up with the answer to THAT, let me know. That's what I have to find out.

"But right now I'm going into town with Marco. See you tonight!"

The Woodlanders and Chief Hemster went out and found Duffy.

Then they drove off to find a copy machine. At the bank, Duffy made copies of the new-found map. He sealed two of them in plastic, to use for diving.

They headed straight for the beach ... parked their cars ... and checked the map one more time.

Dave said, "Look. The zig-zag passageway looks pretty simple ... until you get to this big bend.

"See ... right here ... about halfway to where the gold might be ... the passage-way turns to the left."

Bill said, "And just after that, the tunnel makes a Y shape.

"Look at this second branch to the left again. It comes to a dead end. It would be easy to make a mistake there."

Kathy said, "You'll have to remember to go to the right there, Dave."

Duffy said, "Dave and I will remember. Our lives may depend on it."

He helped Dave into his gear, then put on his own.

He said, "Now, let's go, Dave. Why don't the rest of you bring my boat to the cave? You can anchor near there and swim while you wait."

Mrs. Tandy said, "I can bring the boat over. The rest of you can keep swimming. I've had enough water for today. Maybe Chief Hemster will keep me company in the boat?"

Chief Hemster said, "Of course!"

Bill said, "Wait a minute, everyone. Put some of this on." He held up two bottles of sunscreen.

Sammy said, "Yuck! I hate this stuff! It's as slippery as a rotten banana. And it smells like one, too."

But he grabbed a bottle and put some on.

Then Duffy and Dave headed down into the water.

Duffy led Dave to the cave opening. He handed Dave a light.

They swam through the first tunnel, to the second cave.

It was as black as night.

The only light in that deep, dark place came from the lights they carried.

They swam to the back wall. The openings DID match the map!

They swam to the one marked by the X.

Slowly they entered the tunnel.

Dave thought, "I'm glad it's wide, so Duffy and I can swim side by side."

They made the turn at the big bend. They watched carefully for where the tunnel branched.

They turned safely into the right-hand tunnel.

Dave thought, "I wonder if this is where that swimmer died. Are his bones inside that left-hand tunnel?"

He was scared. He wondered, "Will we be trapped, too?"

Then, suddenly, their light spread out around them. THEY WERE IN A CAVE!

The cave was huge ... and right where the big circle was on the map.

Dave thought, "ORO EN AGUA. Gold in water. Maybe it's really here!"

Water filled most of the cave, but there was a wide, low dome above them.

Dave looked up. He thought, "At least there's some air above the water."

He and Duffy shined their lights all around. The cave was as big as a movie theater!

Then Dave noticed something strange. He could tell there had been a big hole in the dome ... a hole large enough for a person to fit through. Now a big rock rested on it, closing it up.

Duffy was waving for Dave to follow him. They dived deeper under the water.

The coral was shaped into all kinds of bumps and hollows.

They searched every inch of the floor and walls.

They found nothing.

They went over it again.

Nothing.

Finally they floated up to the dome to rest.

They took out their mouth pieces so they could talk.

Dave shined his light up at the dome. He said, "Did you see that hole? I bet THAT'S how the pirates found this hiding place!

"Maybe they cut their way into the jungle to bury their gold. While they were digging, their picks broke through this dome! It was probably an accident!"

Duffy said, "Could be. Still no sign of gold, though."

Dave said, "Maybe the coral grew over it. Or maybe one of the pirates came and stole the gold from the other guys. Then when THEY came, the gold was gone."

Duffy said, "Then if the gold was gone, maybe one of them started looking around for it in the tunnel."

Dave nodded. "I bet that's how he found the passageway to the ocean. Maybe it was even the sailor who wrote the diary and made the maps!

"Whoever it was must have been really brave ... and a great swimmer!"

Dave shined his light around the dome again. He noticed a bump just above the water.

A big piece of coral stuck out of the wall. He touched Duffy and pointed to it. They swam over to look.

Then Dave's heart skipped a beat.

There was something shiny on top of the lump of coral!

But it wasn't pirate gold.

It was a plastic bag!

Dave picked it up.

It was stuffed with tiny glassy stones.

It took him a minute to realize what the stones were.

He looked Duffy right in the eyes.

He said, "I DON'T BELIEVE THIS! THESE LOOK LIKE DIAMONDS!"

Chapter 12:
It's Spy-Catching Time!

Dave was holding the spy diamonds in his hand!

Duffy and Dave swam out to show the others.

Sammy yelled, "Holy catfish!"

In a flash Chief Hemster and Mrs. Tandy pulled up the anchor on the boat and took it back to the beach.

They all piled into their cars.

They raced to the hotel to see if Mr. Sanders was back.

He wasn't there.

They drove to town to look for him.

Sammy said, "Wait, we've got to use some brain power on this. We've got to ask ourselves where he and Marco would be."

He closed his eyes.

Then he yelled, "I've got it! Follow me!"

He ran to a store. He asked, "Do you speak English?"

The woman nodded and smiled.

Sammy said, "Where could we get really big hamburgers?"

She pointed to a little coffee shop a few doors away. Sammy ran into the shop.

In a minute he came running out with Mr. Sanders!

Marco raced out after them. He was finishing a hamburger as he ran.

Dave told them the whole story ... about the diary ... the maps ... the gold hunt ... the watery passageway ... and the plastic bag of diamonds.

He handed the bag to Mr. Sanders.

Mr. Sanders said, "I can't believe this. I really can't believe the luck. I'd never have found the diamonds there in a million years! Now we have to act fast."

Mrs. Tandy said, "What do we need to do?"

Mr. Sanders said, "We have to put the diamonds back where Dave found them."

Sammy yelled, "PUT THEM BACK? No way! Why?"

Mr. Sanders said, "Because Marco remembered something. He says a SECOND boat anchors here, too.

"He says it ALWAYS comes the day after the first one.

"It's called *El Gato.*"

Kathy said, "That means 'the cat,' doesn't it?"

Mr. Sanders nodded. "If Marco's right, *El Gato* will arrive today. And I can guess what they will do. They'll send a diver into that cave.

"Which is why we have to put the

diamonds back. The diver has to find them. Then they'll take them to Florida. And we can catch them in the act back in the U.S."

Kathy said, "But why can't you catch them BEFORE they go?"

Mr. Sanders said, "I can't prove they're breaking the law yet. I have to follow them back to Florida to see the hand-off."

Bill said, "Can we help?"

Mr. Sanders said, "Well, I sure hope so!"

Duffy said, "Count me in if you need me. But you'll have to fill me in on what's going on!"

Mr. Sanders talked to him as they drove back to the beach.

Dave and Duffy got right to work to return the bag of diamonds.

They dived down. They hurried through the outer caves and into the inner tunnel.

But at the bend, Duffy suddenly stopped.

With his light he pointed to his air hose.

Bubbles were coming out of it, fast. It had sprung a leak!

Quickly Dave took a deep breath from his mouthpiece.

Then he held the mouthpiece to Duffy's mouth.

Duffy nodded.

He put one hand on Dave's shoulder. He aimed his light with the other.

Then he kicked to move them both through the water.

Dave moved the mouthpiece between them with one hand.

He swam with the other arm.

Together they reached the air space in the inner cave.

Duffy gasped, "Dave, you just saved my life."

Dave said, "Well, maybe. But I bet you could have held your breath. You could have made it without me."

They put the diamonds back on the coral shelf.

Duffy said, "All right, our job is done. Let's get out of here."

Breathing from Dave's mouthpiece, they made it back out of the cave.

The others were waiting in the water. They cheered as the divers came up.

When they got to the beach, Mr. Sanders said, "Would you be willing to help with the next step?

"I'm afraid this whole business might take several days. It depends on how fast the smugglers travel.

"I have a big fishing boat waiting. The *Stingray*. Marco and I will be on it. I'd like you to go with us.

"You'd look like my fishing party.

Then maybe the smugglers won't suspect I'm following them. And you could help me track them back to Florida."

Kathy said, "I have an idea! Duffy puts radio senders onto turtles to track them. What if he could put one onto *El Gato?*

"Then we could stay out of sight and still follow them."

Sammy said, "Boats aren't turtles. How can he stick a radio to a boat? And what if the spies see him putting the radio on?"

110

Duffy said, "Don't worry, Sammy. I can figure that out."

He turned to Mr. Sanders. He said, "You'll have to promise to return me to Cozumel if I go. I'd have to get back to my turtles."

Mr. Sanders said, "It's a deal. I can send you back the day we dock. How about the rest of you?"

Bill said, "Well ... we planned to hunt gold ... but hunting spies sounds just as exciting to me!"

Dave said, "I'm with you, Bill."

Mrs. Tandy said, "Sounds good to me!"

Sammy said, "Then that's that. Because I go anyplace Bill goes.

"And Kathy will go anyplace Dave goes.

"And Chief Hemster will go anyplace Mrs. Tandy goes!"

Marco added, "And I will go anyplace

Mr. Sanders go!"

Mr. Sanders said, "Then go pack fast, everybody. The hotel car will drive you back here. Dock your boat, Duffy. Let's get going!"

Sammy jumped straight into the air like a kangaroo.

He ran to the car.

He grabbed Dave's wheelchair.

He carried it over his head.

He yelled, "Get in, Dave! Move it, guys! It's spy-catching time!"

Chapter 13:
A Special Fish

The next day, the *Stingray* pulled up to a
pier in Florida.

Sammy jumped off the boat.

He carried his metal fishing box.

Bill and Chief Hemster carried Dave in his wheelchair onto the pier.

The others followed them.

El Gato had just tied up at the next pier ... where people un-loaded fresh fish.

A few at a time, the group from the *Stingray* walked onto that pier.

Dave and Kathy looked over the tables of fish for sale.

Marco, Bill, and Sammy stopped near *El Gato.*

Sammy opened his fishing box. He started checking the gear.

Bill and Marco took things out and looked at them. Sammy slowly put them back, one by one.

Mr. Sanders and Duffy stood watching them.

Chief Hemster and Mrs. Tandy went walking toward the pier's end.

All seemed peaceful.

114

Soon two men got off *El Gato*. A third man stayed on board.

He handed down a few boxes of fish.

Next to the other fish, their fish looked old and dry.

A few buyers took a look. They walked away quickly!

Sammy whispered, "Those guys must be crazy! They'll never sell their fish. These fish are disGUSTing!"

But a buyer did come along. He took a look at their disgusting fish. Then he said, "I need a special fish for a special party."

One of the *El Gato* men said, "I have such a fish back on the boat."

He called, "Hey! Hand me that special fish, the one I wrapped. It's in a brown package."

The man still on the boat passed a package down to him.

He handed it to the fish buyer.

Then everything happened at once.

Mr. Sanders shouted, "Stay where you are!"

A police officer came from the side. He yelled, "Freeze! Police!"

But the man who took the package began running down the pier. He hugged the fish against his chest like a football.

Dave yelled, "Here we go, Kathy!"

He zoomed down the pier in his wheelchair and knocked the man over.

As the man fell, he threw the package into the water.

Sammy yelled like Tarzan.

Feet first, he jumped into the water. He grabbed the package before it sank.

The man on *El Gato* jumped into the ocean, too, in a half-dive.

He hit his head on something.

He didn't come back up.

Duffy and Bill jumped in after him.

They found him and pulled him up.

Three more plain-clothes police officers ran onto the pier.

They snapped handcuffs on the fish buyer, who was lying near Dave. They read him his rights.

They ran toward the two diamond smugglers still standing near the boat.

They handcuffed one. But the other one darted away.

A police officer chased after him.

The smuggler dumped over a table of fish. The table hit Mr. Sanders.

Chief Hemster grabbed hold of the man. He held on like a bulldog. They both fell into a pile of icy fish.

The ice was slippery.

The smuggler got away from Chief Hemster.

Marco grabbed a frozen fish as big as a baseball bat.

He yelled, "You bad guy! You hurt Mr. Sanders! I will get you!"

WHACK!

He hit the man right on the head. The man lay still.

The police put handcuffs on him ... and pulled him over to the sandy beach.

Then Bill called from the water, "What

should we do with this one?"

Mr. Sanders called, "Pull him to the beach, too."

Sammy was waiting there with the package.

Mr. Sanders opened it.

Inside was a big fish.

Its stomach had a cut in it.

The diamond bag was sticking out of the fish's stomach.

Sammy held his nose. He said, "Boy, that fish stinks!"

Mr. Sanders handed it to a Florida police officer.

He said, "Here, get this into a freezer. You'll need it in court. Take it away with those crooks, and fast. Let's get rid of that SMELL!"

The police drove off.

Sammy let go of his nose. After one sniff, he took hold of it again.

He said, "Something STILL stinks!"

Mrs. Tandy said, "I hate to tell you this, honey. I think it's us! We have fish juice all over us. We are spoiling in the sun!"

Bill said, "We can't ride back to the condo smelling like this. Follow me, guys."

He and Sammy took Dave. The others followed them into the water, clothes and all. They came out clean!

Then Mr. Sanders said, "Well, we better get Duffy back to his turtles. But there's a three-hour wait for his plane."

He drove them to the condo where the Woodlanders had started their trip. They changed into dry clothes.

Bill found a giant box of cookies in the kitchen.

Then they sat down at the table.

Dave said, "I'm sorry we never found the pirate gold, Duffy.

"The money could have helped you with your turtle work ... your boats ... your diving gear ... your trips.

"But remember, there is that pyramid we told you about. You could look there for gold after we leave."

Mr. Sanders said, "Oh, but you DID find treasure. I didn't want to tell you until after we'd caught the spies for sure.

But there's a reward for catching those guys!

"The Woodlanders, and you, Duffy, will share it."

Sammy shouted, "A REWARD! Great! The first thing we can buy is more of these cookies!" And he chewed up another one.

Bill said, "But what about you, Mr. Sanders? And Chief Hemster?"

Mr. Sanders said, "We can't take reward money for doing our jobs. But I did get another reward ... the best of all!

"Marco says he wants to live with my wife and me. We will have to ask the government to let him stay here in the U.S. But I think we can swing it."

Marco said, "You find out I am very, very good son. I not much trouble. And if your house too crowded, I sleep on the sidewalk. That OK?"

Mr. Sanders lifted Marco up into his arms and hugged him.

Mrs. Tandy said, "Don't worry, Marco. None of us will ever let you sleep on the sidewalk again."

They all crowded around him.

Then, from the middle of the pile-up came Marco's little voice.

He said, "After the hugs, can I have another cookie?"

everyone laughed.

And sitting on Mr. Sanders' lap, eating a cookie, OK-Marco was really OK at last.

And the Woodlanders sat and looked at their three new friends.

The treasure map had worked after all!